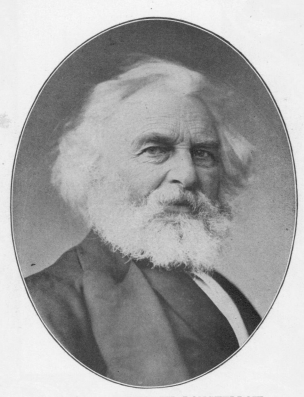

HENRY WADSWORTH LONGFELLOW.

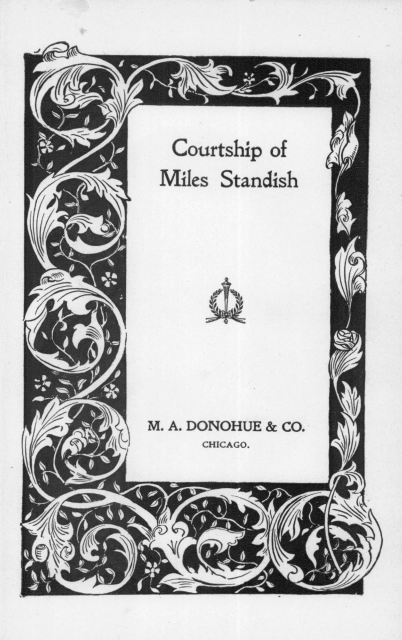

Courtship of Miles Standish

M. A. DONOHUE & CO.

CHICAGO.

THE
COURTSHIP OF MILES STANDISH

I.

MILES STANDISH.

N the Old Colony days, in Plymouth the land of the Pilgrims,

To and fro in a room of his simple and primitive dwelling,

Clad in doublet and hose, and boots of Cordovan leather,

Strode, with a martial air, Miles Standish
the Puritan Captain.

Buried in thought he seemed, with his hands
behind him, and pausing   5

Ever and anon to behold his glittering weapons of warfare,

Hanging in shining array along the walls
of the chamber,—

Cutlass and corslet of steel, and his trusty
sword of Damascus,

Curved at the point and inscribed with its
mystical Arabic sentence,

While underneath, in a corner, were fowling-
piece, musket, and matchlock.   10

Short of stature he was, but strongly built
and athletic,

Broad in the shoulders, deep-chested, with
    muscles and sinews of iron;

Brown as a nut was his face, but his russet
    beard was already

Flaked with patches of snow, as hedges
    sometimes in November.

Near him was seated John Alden, his friend,
    and household companion,   15

Writing with diligent speed at a table of pine
    by the window;

Fair-haired, azure-eyed, with delicate Saxon
    complexion,

Having the dew of his youth, and the beauty
    thereof, as the captives

Whom Saint Gregory saw, and exclaimed,
    "Not Angles but Angels."

Youngest of all was he of the men who came

   in the May Flower.   20

  Suddenly breaking the silence, the diligent

   scribe interrupting,

Spake, in the pride of his heart, Miles Stan-

   dish the Captain of Plymouth.

"Look at these arms," he said, "the warlike

   weapons that hang here

Burnished and bright and clean, as if for pa-

   rade or inspection!

This is the sword of Damascus I fought

   with in Flanders; this breastplate,   25

Well I remember the day! once saved my

   life in a skirmish;

Here in front you can see the very dint of

   the bullet

Fired point-blank at my heart by a Spanish
arcabucero.

Had it not been of sheer steel, the forgotten
bones of Miles Standish

Would at this moment be mould, in their
grave in the Flemish morasses." 30

Thereupon answered John Alden, but looked
not up from his writing:

"Truly the breath of the Lord hath slack-
ened the speed of the bullet;

He in his mercy preserved you, to be our
shield and our weapon!"

Still the Captain continued, unheeding the
words of the stripling:

"See, how bright they are burnished, as if
in an arsenal hanging; 35

That is because I have done it myself, and
  not left it to others.

Serve yourself, would you be well served,
  is an excellent adage;

So I take care of my arms, as you of your
  pens and your inkhorn.

Then, too, there are my soldiers, my great,
  invincible army,

Twelve men, all equipped, having each his
  rest and his matchlock,   4c

Eighteen shillings a month, together with
  diet and pillage,

And, like Cæsar, I know the name of each
  of my soldiers!"

This he said with a smile, that danced in
  his eyes, as the sunbeams

Dance on the waves of the sea, and vanish

again in a moment.

Alden laughed as he wrote, and still the Cap-

tain continued : 45

"Look! you can see from this window my

brazen howitzer planted

High on the roof of the church, a preacher

who speaks to the purpose,

Steady, straight-forward, and strong, with

irresistible logic,

Orthodox, flashing conviction right into the

hearts of the heathen.

Now we are ready, I think, for any assault

of the Indians; 50

Let them come, if
they like, and the
sooner they try it
the better,—
Let them come, if
they like, be it
sagamore, sachem
or pow-wow,
Aspinet,   Samoset,
Corbitant, Squanto, or Tokamaha-
mon!"

Long at the window he stood, and wist-
fully gazed on the landscape,
Washed with a cold gray mist, the vapory
breath of the east-wind,   55

Forest and meadow and hill, and the steel-
    blue rim of the ocean,

Lying silent and sad, in the afternoon shad-
    ows and sunshine.

Over his countenance flitted a shadow like
    those on the landscape,

Gloom intermingled with light; and his voice
    was subdued with emotion,

Tenderness, pity, regret, as after a pause he
    proceeded :

"Yonder there, on the hill by the sea, lies
    buried Rose Standish;   60

Beautiful rose of love, that bloomed for me
    by the wayside!

She was the first to die of all who came in
    the May Flower!

Green above her is growing the field of wheat
    we have sown there,
Better to hide from the Indian scouts the
    graves of our people,
Lest they should count them and see how
    many already have perished!''   65
Sadly his face he averted, and strode up and
    down, and was thoughtful.

Fixed to the opposite wall was a shelf of
    books, and among them
Prominent three, distinguished alike for bulk
    and for binding;
Bariffe's Artillery Guide, and the Commen-
    taries of Cæsar,
Out of the Latin translated by Arthur Gold-
    ing of London,   70

And, as if guarded by these, between them
was standing the Bible.

Musing a moment before them, Miles Standish paused, as if doubtful

Which of the three he should choose for his
consolation and comfort,

Whether the wars of the Hebrews, the fa-
mous campaigns of the Romans,

Or the Artillery practice, designed for bel-
ligerent Christians. 75

Finally down from its shelf he dragged the
ponderous Roman,

Seated himself at the window, and opened
the book, and in silence

Turned o'er the well-worn leaves, where
thumbmarks thick on the margin,

Like the trample of feet, proclaimed the battle was hottest.

Nothing was heard in the room but the hurrying pen of the stripling,   80

Busily writing epistles important, to go by
the May Flower,

Ready to sail on the
morrow, or next
day at latest, God
willing!

Homeward bound with the tidings of all that
terrible winter,

Letters written by Alden, and full of the
name of Priscilla,

Full of the name and the fame of the Puritan maiden Priscilla!   85

II.

LOVE AND FRIENDSHIP.

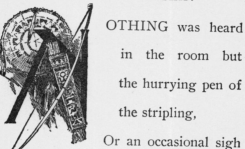

OTHING was heard in the room but the hurrying pen of the stripling,

Or an occasional sigh from the laboring heart of the Captain,

Reading the marvelous words and achievements of Julius Cæsar.

After a while he exclaimed, as he smote with his hand, palm downwards,

Heavily on the page: "A wonderful man was this Cæsar!

15

5

You are a writer, and I am a fighter, but here

    is a fellow

Who could both write and fight, and in both

    was equally skilful!"

Straightway answered and spake John Al-

    den, the comely, the youthful:

"Yes, he was equally skilled, as you say, with

    his pen and his weapons.

Somewhere have I read, but where I forget,

    he could dictate   10

Seven letters at once, at the same time writ-

    ing his memoirs."

"Truly," continued the Captain, not heeding

    or hearing the other,

"Truly a wonderful man was Caius Julius

    Cæsar!

Better be first, he said, in a little Iberian

    village,

Than be second in Rome, and I think he was

    right when he said it.   15

Twice was he married before he was twenty,

    and many times after;

Battles five hundred he fought, and a thou-

    sand cities he conquered;

He, too, fought in Flanders, as he himself

    has recorded;

Finally he was stabbed by his friend, the

    orator Brutus!

Now, do you know what he did on a certain

    occasion in Flanders,   20

When the rear-guard of his army retreated,

    the front giving way too,

And the immortal Twelfth Legion was

    crowded so closely together

There was no room for their swords? Why,

    he seized a shield from a soldier,

Put himself straight at the head of his troops,

    and commanded the captains,

Calling on each by his name, to order for-

    ward the ensigns;   25

Then to widen the ranks, and give more room

    for their weapons;

So he won the day, the battle of something-

    or-other.

That's what I always say; if you wish a

    thing to be well done,

You must do it yourself, you must not leave

    it to others!"

All was silent again; the Captain contin-
    ued his reading.   30

Nothing was heard in the room but the
    hurrying pen of the stripling

Writing epistles important to go next day by
    the May Flower,

Filled with the name and the fame of the
    Puritan maiden Priscilla;

Every sentence began or closed with the name
    of Priscilla,

Till the treacherous pen, to which he con-
    fided the secret,   35

Strove to betray it by singing and shouting
    the name of Priscilla!

Finally closing his book, with a bang of the
    ponderous cover,

Sudden and loud as the sound of a soldier

    grounding his musket,

Thus to the young man spake Miles Stan-

    dish the Captain of Plymouth:

"When you have finished your work, I have

    something important to tell you.   40

Be not however in haste; I can wait; I shall

  not be impatient!"

Straightway Alden replied, as he folded the

  last of his letters,

Pushing his papers aside, and giving respect-

  ful attention:

"Speak; for whenever you speak, I am al-

  ways ready to listen,

Always ready to hear whatever pertains to

  Miles Standish."   45

Thereupon answered the Captain, embar-

  rassed, and culling his phrases:

" 'Tis not good for a man to be alone, say

  the Scriptures.

This I have said before, and again and again

  I repeat it;

Every hour in tne day, I think it, and feel it,

    and say it.

Since Rose Standish died, my life has been

    weary and dreary: 5ᴄ

Sick at heart have I been, beyond the healing

    of friendship.

Oft in my lonely hours have I thought of the

    maiden Priscilla.

She is alone in the world; her father and

    mother and brother

Died in the winter together; I saw her going

    and coming,

Now to the grave of the dead, and now to the

    bed of the dying,   55

Patient, courageous, and strong, and said **to**

    myself, that if ever

There were angels on earth, as there are
    angels in heaven,

Two have I seen and known; and the angel
    whose name is Priscilla

Holds in my desolate life the place which
    the other abandoned.

Long have I cherished the thought, but
    never have dared to reveal it,   60

Being a coward in this, though valiant
    enough for the most part.

Go to the damsel Priscilla, the loveliest
    maiden of Plymouth,

Say that a blunt old Captain, a man not of
    words but of actions,

Offers his hand and his heart, the hand and
    heart of a soldier.

Not in these words, you know, but this in
    short is my meaning;   65

I am a maker of war, and not a maker of
    phrases.

You, who are bred as a scholar, can say it in
    elegant language,

Such as you read in your books of the plead-
    ings and wooings of lovers,

Such as you think best adapted to win the
    heart of a maiden."

When he had spoken, John Alden, the fair-
    haired, taciturn stripling,   70

All aghast at his words, surprised, embar-
    rassed, bewildered,

Trying to mask his dismay by treating the subject with lightness,

Trying to smile, and yet feeling his heart stand still in his bosom,

Just as a timepiece stops in a house that is stricken by lightning,

Thus made answer and spake, or rather stammered than answered: 75

"Such a message as that, I am sure I should mangle and mar it;

If you would have it well done,—I am only repeating your maxim,—

You must do it yourself, you must not leave it to others!"

But with the air of a man whom nothing can
    turn from his purpose,
Gravely shaking his head, made answer the
    Captain of Plymouth: 80
"Truly the maxim is good, and I do not mean
    to gainsay it;
But we must use it discreetly, and not waste
    powder for nothing.
Now, as I said before, I was never a maker of
    phrases.
I can march up to a fortress and summon the
    place to surrender,
But march up to a woman with such a propo-
    sal, I dare not.   85
I'm not afraid of bullets, nor shot from the
    mouth of a cannon,

But of a thundering "No!" point-blank from
the mouth of a woman,

That I confess I'm afraid of, nor am I
ashamed to confess it!

So you must grant my request, for you are an
elegant scholar,

Having the graces of speech, and skill in the
turning of phrases." 90

Taking the hand of his friend, who still was
reluctant and doubtful,

Holding it long in his own, and pressing it
kindly, he added:

"Though I have spoken thus lightly, yet deep
is the feeling that prompts me;

Surely you cannot refuse what I ask in the
name of our friendship!"

Then made answer John Alden: "The name
    of friendship is sacred;   95
What you demand in that name, I have not
    the power to deny you!"
So the strong will prevailed, subduing and
    moulding the gentler,
Friendship prevailed over love, and Alden
    went on his errand.

III.

THE LOVER'S ERRAND.

O the strong will pre-vailed, and Alden went on his errand,

Out of the street of the village, and into the paths of the forest,

Into the tranquil woods, where blue-birds and robins were building

Towns in the populous trees, with hanging gardens of verdure,

Peaceful, aerial cities

of joy and affection

and freedom.   5

All around him was

calm, but within

him   commotion

and conflict,

Love contending with

friendship, and self

with each generous

impulse.

To and fro in his breast his thoughts were

heaving and dashing,

As in a foundering ship, with every roll of the

vessel,

Washes the bitter sea, the merciless surge of
the ocean! 10
"Must I relinquish it all," he cried with a
wild lamentation,
"Must I relinquish it all, the joy, the hope, the
illusion?
Was it for this I have loved and waited, and
worshipped in silence?
Was it for this I have followed the flying feet
and the shadow
Over the wintry sea, to the desolate shores of
New England? 15
Truly the heart is deceitful, and out of its
depths of corruption
Rise, like an exhalation, the misty phantoms
of passion;

Angels of light they seem, but are only delu-
    sions of Satan.

All is clear to me now; I feel it, I see it dis-
    tinctly!

This is the hand of the Lord; it is laid upon
    me in anger,   20

For I have followed too much the heart's de-
    sires and devices,

Worshipping Astaroth blindly, and impious
    idols of Baal.

This is the cross I must bear; the sin and the
    swift retribution."

So through the Plymouth woods **John Alden** went on his errand;

Crossing the brook at the ford, where it

brawled over pebble and shallow, 25

Gathering still, as he went, the May-flowers

blooming around him,

Fragrant, filling the air with a strange and

wonderful sweetness,

Children lost in the woods, and covered with

leaves in their slumber.

"Puritan flowers," he said, "and the type of

Puritan maidens,

Modest and simple and sweet, the very type

of Priscilla ! 30

So I will take them to her; to Priscilla the

May-flower of Plymouth,

Modest and simple
and sweet, as a
parting gift will I
take them;

Breathing their silent farewells, as they fade
and wither and perish,

Soon to be thrown away as is the heart of the
giver."

So through the Plymouth woods John Alden
went on his errand;   35

Came to an open space, and saw the disk of
the ocean,

Sailless, sombre and cold with the comfort-
less breath of the east-wind;

Saw the new-built house, and people at work
in a meadow;

Heard, as he drew near the door, the musical

> voice of Priscilla

Singing the hundredth Psalm, the grand old

> Puritan anthem, 40

Music that Luther sang to the sacred words

> of the Psalmist,

Full of the breath of the Lord, consoling and

> comforting many.

Then, as he opened the door, he beheld the

> form of the maiden

Seated beside her wheel, and the carded wool

> like a snow-drift

Piled at her knee, her white hands feeding

> the ravenous spindle, 45

While with her foot on the treadle she guided

> the wheel in its motion.

Open wide on her lap lay the well-worn
psalm-book of Ainsworth ,

Printed in Amsterdam, the words and the
music together,

Rough-hewn, angular notes, like stones in the
wall of a churchyard,

Darkened and overhung by the running vine
of the verses.   50

Such was the book from whose pages she
sang the old Puritan anthem,

She, the Puritan girl, in the solitude of the
forest,

Making the humble house and the modest ap-
parel of home-spun

Beautiful with her beauty, and rich with the
wealth of her being!

Over him rushed, like a wind that is keen
and cold and relentless,   55

Thoughts of what might have been, and the
weight and woe of his errand;

All the dreams that had faded, and all the
hopes that had vanished,

All his life henceforth a dreary and tenant-
less mansion,

Haunted by vain regrets, and pallid, sorrow-
ful faces.

Still he said to himself, and almost fiercely he
said it,   60

"Let not him that putteth his hand to the
plough look backwards;

Though the ploughshare cut through the
flowers of life to its fountains,

Though it pass o'er the graves of the dead
and the hearths of the living,

It is the will of the Lord; and his mercy en-
dureth for ever!"

So he entered the
house; and the
hum of the
wheel and the
singing 65

Suddenly ceased; for Priscilla, aroused by
his step on the threshold,

Rose as he entered, and gave him her hand,
in signal of welcome,

Saying, "I knew it was you, when I heard
your step in the passage;

For I was thinking of you, as I sat there sing-
    ing and spinning."

Awkward and dumb with delight, that a
    thought of him had been mingled   70

Thus in the sacred psalm, that came from the
    heart of the maiden,

Silent before her he stood, and gave her the
    flowers for an answer,

Finding no words for his thought. He re-
    membered that day in the winter,

After the first great snow, when he broke a
    path from the village,

Reeling and plunging along through the
    drifts that encumbered the doorway,   75

Stamping the snow from his feet as he en-
    tered the house, and Priscilla

Laughed at his snowy locks, and gave him a
  seat by the fireside,
Grateful and pleased to know he had thought
  of her in the snow-storm.
Had he but spoken then! perhaps not in vain
  had he spoken;
Now it was all too late; the golden moment
  had vanished!   8o
So he stood there abashed, and gave her the
  flowers for an answer.

Then they sat down and talked of the birds
  and the beautiful Spring-time,
Talked of their friends at home, and the May
  Flower that sailed on the morrow

"I have been thinking all day," said gently
the Puritan maiden,
"Dreaming all night, and thinking all day,
of the hedge-rows of England,— 85

They are in blossom now, and the country is
all like a garden;

Thinking of lanes and fields, and the song of
    the lark and the linnet,
Seeing the village street, and familiar faces
    of neighbors
Going about as of old, and stopping to gossip
    together,
And, at the end of the street, the village
    church, with the ivy

90

Climbing the old gray tower, and the quiet
    graves in the churchyard.
Kind are the people I live with, and dear to
    me my religion;
Still my heart is so sad, that I wish myself
    back in Old England.
You will say it is wrong, but I cannot help it:
    I almost

Wish myself back in Old England, I feel so

lonely and wretched."   95

Thereupon answered the youth :—"Indeed

I do not condemn you;

Stouter hearts than a woman's have quailed

in this terrible winter.

Yours is tender and trusting, and needs a

stronger to lean on;

So I have come to you now, with an offer and

proffer of marriage

Made by a good man and true, Miles Stand-

ish the Captain of Plymouth!"   100

Thus he delivered his message, the dexterous

writer of letters,—

Did not embellish the theme, nor array it in
beautiful phrases,

But came straight to the point, and blurted it
out like a schoolboy;

Even the Captain himself could hardly have
said it more bluntly.

Mute with amazement and sorrow, Priscilla
    the Puritan maiden   105
Looked into Alden's face, her eyes dilated
    with wonder,
Feeling his words like a blow, that stunned
    her and rendered her speechless;
Till at length she exclaimed, interrupting the
    ominous silence:
"If the great Captain of Plymouth is so very
    eager to wed me,
Why does he not come himself, and take the
    trouble to woo me?
If I am not worth the wooing, I surely am
    not worth the winning!"
Then John Alden began explaining and
    smoothing the matter,

Making it worse as he went, by saying the
  Captain was busy,—
Had no time for such things;—such things!
  the words grating harshly
Fell on the ear of Priscilla; and swift as a
  flash she made answer: 115
"Has he no time for such things, as you call
  it, before he is married,
Would he be likely to find it, or make it,
  after the wedding?
That is the way with you men; you don't un-
  derstand us, you cannot.
When you have made up your minds, after
  thinking of this one and that one,
Choosing, selecting, rejecting, comparing
  one with another,   120

Then you make known your desire, with
    abrupt and sudden avowal,

And are offended and hurt, and indignant
    perhaps, that a woman

Does not respond at once to a love that she
    never suspected,

Does not attain at a bound the height to
    which you have been climbing.

This is not right nor just: for surely a
    woman's affection   125

Is not a thing to be asked for, and had for
    only the asking.

When one is truly in love, one not only says
    it, but shows it.

Had he but waited awhile, had he only
    showed that he loved me,

Even this Captain of yours—who knows?—
at last might have won me,
Old and rough as he is; but now it never
can happen."   130

Still John Alden went on, unheeding the
words of Priscilla,
Urging the suit of his friend, explaining, per-
suading, expanding;
Spoke of his courage and skill, and of all his
battles in Flanders,
How with the people of God he had chosen to
suffer affliction,
How, in return for his zeal, they had made
him Captain of Plymouth;   135

He was a gentleman born, could trace his ped-
　　igree plainly
Back to Hugh Standish of Duxbury Hall, in
　　Lancashire, England,
Who was the son of Ralph, and the grandson
　　of Thurston de Standish;
Heir unto vast estates, of which he was base-
　　ly defrauded,
Still bore the family arms, and had for his
　　crest a cock argent　　　　　　　140

Combed and wat-
tled gules, and all
the rest of the
blazon.

He was a man of
honor, of noble and generous nature;

Though he was rough, he was kindly; she
    knew how during the winter

He had attended the sick, with a hand as gen-
    tle as woman's;

Somewhat hasty and hot, he could not deny
    it, and headstrong,   145

Stern as a soldier might be, but hearty, and
    placable always,

Not to be laughed at and scorned, because he
    was little of stature;

For he was great of heart, magnanimous,
    courtly, courageous;

Any woman in Plymouth, nay, any woman
    in England,

Might be happy and proud to be called the
    wife of Miles Standish!   150

But as he warmed and glowed, in his sim-
    ple and eloquent language,
Quite forgetful of self, and full of the praise
    of his rival,
Archly the maiden smiled, and, with eyes
    over-running with laughter,
Said, in a tremulous voice, "Why don't you
    speak for yourself, John?"

IV.

JOHN ALDEN.

NTO the open air
John Alden, per-
plexed and be-
wildered,

Rushed like a man insane, and wandered
alone by the sea-side;

Paced up and down the sands, and bared his
head to the east-wind,

Cooling his heated brow, and the fire and
fever within him.

Slowly as out of the
heavens, with apoca-
lyptical splendors,   5
Sank the City of God,
in the vision of John
the Apostle,
So, with its cloudy walls
of chrysolite, jasper,
and sapphire,
Sank the broad red sun,
and over its turrets
uplifted
Glimmered the golden
reed of the angel who
measured the city.

"Welcome, O wind of the East!" he exclaimed in his wild exultation,   10
"Welcome, O wind of the East, from the
caves of the misty Atlantic!
Blowing o'er fields of dulse, and measure-
less meadows of sea-grass,
Blowing o'er rocky wastes, and the grottos
and gardens of ocean!
Lay thy cold, moist hand on my burning forehead, and wrap me
Close in thy garments of mist, to allay the
fever within me!"   15

Like an awakened conscience, the sea was
moaning and tossing,

Beating remorseful and loud the mutable
    sands of the sea-shore.

Fierce in his soul was the struggle and tumult
    of passions contending;

Love triumphant and crowned, and friend-
    ship wounded and bleeding,

Passionate cries of desire, and importunate
    pleadings of duty!   20

"Is it my fault," he said, "that the maiden
    has chosen between us?

Is it my fault that he failed,—my fault that I
    am the victor?"

Then within him there thundered a voice, like
    the voice of the Prophet:

"It hath displeased the Lord!"—and he
    thought of David's transgression,

Bathsheba's beautiful face, and his friend in

the front of the battle!   25

Shame and confusion of guilt, and abasement

and self-condemnation,

Overwhelmed him at once; and he cried in

the deepest contrition:

"It hath displeased the Lord! It is the temp-

tation of Satan!"

Then, uplifting his head, he looked at the

sea, and beheld there

Dimly the shadowy form of the May Flower

riding at anchor,   30

Rocked on the rising tide, and ready to sail

on the morrow;

Heard the voices of men through the mist,
the rattle of cordage

Thrown on the deck, the shouts of the mate,
and the sailors' "Ay, ay, Sir!"

Clear and distinct, but not loud, in the drip-
ping air of the twilight.

Still for a moment he stood, and listened,
and stared at the vessel,   35

Then went hurriedly on, as one who, seeing
a phantom,

Stops, then quickens his pace, and follows the
beckoning shadow.

"Yes, it is plain to me now," he murmured;
"the hand of the Lord is

Leading me out of the land of darkness, the
bondage of error,

Through the sea, that shall lift the walls of

its waters around me,   40

Hiding me, cutting me off, from **the cruel**

thoughts that pursue me.

Back will **I** go o'er the ocean, this dreary land

will abandon,

Her whom I may not love, and him whom **my**

heart has offended.

Better to be in my grave in the green old
    churchyard in England,

Close by my mother's side, and among the
    dust of my kindred;   45

Better be dead and forgotten, than living in
    shame and dishonor!

Sacred and safe and unseen, in the dark of the
    the narrow chamber

With me my secret shall lie, like a buried
    jewel that glimmers

Bright on the hand that is dust, in the cham-
    bers of silence and darkness,—

Yes, as the marriage ring of the great espou-
    sal hereafter!"   50

Thus as he spake, he turned, in the
strength of his strong resolution,
Leaving behind him the shore, and hurried
along in the twilight,

Through the congenial gloom of the forest
silent and sombre,

Till he beheld the lights in the seven houses
    of Plymouth,

Shining like seven stars in the dusk and mist
    of the evening.   55

Soon he entered his door, and found the re-
    doubtable Captain

Sitting alone, and absorbed in the martial
    pages of Caesar,

Fighting some great campaign in Hainault or
    Brabant or Flanders.

"Long have you been on your errand," he
    said with a cheery demeanor,

Even as one who is waiting an answer, and
    fears not the issue.   60

"Not far off is the house, although the woods
    are between us;

But you have lingered so long, that while you
　　were going and coming
I have fought ten battles and sacked and de-
　　molished a city.
Come, sit down, and in order relate to me all
　　that has happened."

Then John Alden spake, and related the
　　wondrous adventure,　　　　　　　65
From beginning to end, minutely, just as it
　　happened;
How he had seen Priscilla, and how he had
　　sped in his courtship,
Only smoothing a little, and softening down
　　her refusal.

But when he came at length to the words
Priscilla had spoken,

Words so tender and cruel: "Why don't you
speak for yourself, John?"   70

Up leaped the Captain of Plymouth, and
stamped on the floor, till his armor

Clanged on the wall, where it hung, with a
sound of sinister omen.

All his pent-up wrath burst forth in a sudden explosion,

Even as a hand-grenade, that scatters destruction around it.

Wildly he shouted, and loud: "John Alden!
you have betrayed me!   75

Me, Miles Standish, your friend! have sup-
planted, defrauded, betrayed me!

One of my ancestors ran his sword through

the heart of Wat Tyler;

Who shall prevent me from running my own

through the heart of a traitor?

Yours is the greater treason, for yours is a

treason to friendship!

You, who lived under my roof, whom I cher-

ished and loved as a brother;   8c

You, who have fed at my board, and drunk at

my cup, to whose keeping

I have entrusted my honor, my thoughts the

most sacred and secret,—

You too, Brutus! ah woe to the name of
    friendship hereafter!
Brutus was Cæsar's friend, and you were
    mine, but henceforward
Let there be nothing between us save war,
    and implacable hatred!"   85

So spake the Captain of Plymouth, and
    strode about in the chamber,
Chafing and choking with rage; like cords
    were the veins on his temples.
But in the midst of his anger a man appeared
    at the doorway,
Bringing in uttermost haste a message of ur-
    gent importance,

Rumors of danger and war and hostile incur-
    sions of Indians!   90
Straightway the Captain paused, and, with-
    out further question or parley,
Took from the nail on the wall his sword
    with its scabbard of iron,
Buckled the belt round his waist, and, frown-
    ing fiercely, departed.
Alden was left alone.   He heard the clank of
    the scabbard
Growing fainter and fainter, and dying away
    in the distance.   95
Then he arose from his seat, and looked forth
    into the darkness,
Felt the cool air blow on his cheek, that was
    hot with the insult,

Lifted his eyes to the heavens, and, folding
his hands as in childhood,
Prayed in the silence of night to the Father
who seeth in secret.

Meanwhile the choleric Captain strode
wrathfully away to the council,   100
Found it already assembled, impatiently
waiting his coming;
Men in the middle of life, austere and grave
in deportment,
Only one of them old, the hill that was near-
est to heaven,
Covered with snow, but erect, the excellent
Elder of Plymouth.

God had sifted three kingdoms to find the
    wheat for this planting,   105
Then had sifted the wheat, as the living seed
    of a nation;
So say the chronicles old, and such is the faith
    of the people!
Near them was standing an Indian, in at-
    titude stern and defiant,
Naked down to the waist, and grim and fero-
    cious in aspect;
While on the table before them was lying un-
    opened a Bible,   110
Ponderous, bound in leather, brass-studded,
    printed in Holland,
And beside it outstretched the skin of a rattle-
    snake glittered,

Filled, like a quiver,
with arrows; a
signal and chal-
lenge of warfare,
Brought by the In-
dian, and speak-
ing with arrowy tongues of defiance.

This Miles Standish beheld, as he entered,
and heard them debating   115
What were an answer befitting the hostile
message and menace,
Talking of this and of that, contriving, sug-
gesting, objecting;
One voice only for peace, and that the voice
of the Elder,

Judging it wise and well that some at least
were converted,

Rather than any were slain, for this was but
Christian behavior!   120

Then outspake Miles Standish, the stalwart
Captain of Plymouth,

Muttering deep in his throat, for his voice
was husky with anger,

"What! do you mean to make war with milk
and the water of roses?

Is it to shoot red squirrels you have your
howitzer planted

There on the roof of the church, or is it to
shoot red devils?   125

Truly the only tongue that is understood by a
savage

Must be the tongue of fire that speaks from
    the mouth of the cannon!"

Thereupon answered and said the excellent
    Elder of Plymouth,

Somewhat amazed and alarmed at this irrev-
    erent language:

"Not so thought Saint Paul, nor yet the other
    Apostles;   130

Not from the cannon's mouth were the
    tongues of fire they spake with!"

But unheeded fell this mild rebuke on the
    Captain,

Who had advanced to the table, and thus con-
    tinued discoursing:

"Leave this matter to me, for to me by right
    it pertaineth.

War is a terrible trade; but in the cause that

is righteous,   135

Sweet is the smell of powder; and thus I an-

swer the challenge!"

Then from the rattlesnake's skin, with a

sudden, contemptuous gesture,

Jerking the Indian arrows, he filled it with

powder and bullets

Full to the very jaws, and handed it back to

the savage,

Saying, in thundering tones: "Here, take it!

this is your answer!"   140

Silently out of the room then glided the glis-

tening savage,

Bearing the serpent's skin, and seeming him-

self like a serpent,

Winding his sinuous way in the dark to the

depths of the forest.

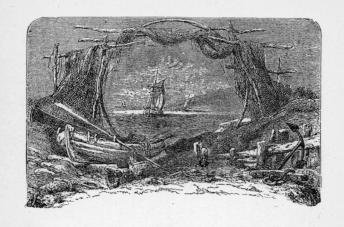

V.

THE SAILING OF THE MAY FLOWER.

UST in the gray of the dawn, as the mists uprose from the meadows,

There was a stir and a sound in the slumbering village of Plymouth;

Clanging and clicking of arms, and the order

imperative, "Forward!"

Given in tone suppressed, a tramp of feet, and

then silence.

Figures ten, in the mist, marched slowly out

of the village. 5

Standish the stalwart it was, with eight of his

valorous army,

Led by their Indian guide, by Hobomok,

friend of the white men,

Northward marching to quell the sudden re-

volt of the savage.

Giants they seemed in the mist, or the mighty

men of King David;

Giants in heart they were, who believed in

God and the Bible,— 10

Ay, who believed in the smiting of Midianites
and Philistines.

Over them gleamed far off the crimson banners of morning;

Under them loud on the sands, the serried
billows, advancing,

Fired along the line, and in regular order retreated.

Many a mile had they marched, when at
    length the village of Plymouth   15
Woke from its sleep, and arose, intent on its
    manifold labors.
Sweet was the air and soft; and slowly the
    smoke from the chimneys
Rose over roofs of thatch, and pointed stead-
    ily eastward;
Men came forth from the doors, and paused
    and talked of the weather,
Said that the wind had changed, and was
    blowing fair for the May Flower;   20
Talked of their Captain's departure, and all
    the dangers that menaced,
He being gone, the town, and what should be
    done in his absence.

Merrily sang the birds, and the tender voices
of women

Consecrated with hymns the common cares of
the household.

Out of the sea rose the sun, and the billows
rejoiced at his coming;   25

Beautiful were his feet on the purple tops of
the mountains;

Beautiful on the sails of the May Flower riding at anchor,

Battered and blackened and worn by all the
storms of the winter.

Loosely against her masts was hanging and
flapping her canvas,

Rent by so many gales, and patched by the
hands of the sailors.   30

Suddenly from her side, as the sun rose over
the ocean,

Darted a puff of smoke, and floated seaward;
anon rang

Loud over field and forest the cannon's roar,
and the echoes

Heard and repeated the sound, the signal-
gun of departure!

Ah, but with louder echoes replied the hearts
of the people!   35

Meekly, in voices subdued, the chapter was
read from the Bible,

Meekly the prayer was begun, but ended in
fervent entreaty!

Then from their houses in haste came forth
the Pilgrims of Plymouth,

Men and women and children, all hurrying
    down to the sea-shore,
Eager, with tearful eyes, to say farewell to
    the May Flower,   40
Homeward bound o'er the sea, and leaving
    them here in the desert.

Foremost among them was Alden. All
    night he had lain without slumber,
Turning and tossing about in the heat and
    unrest of his fever.
He had beheld Miles Standish, who came
    back late from the council,
Stalking into the room, and heard him mutter
    and murmur,   45

Sometimes it seemed a prayer, and sometimes

it sounded like swearing.

Once he had come to the bed, and stood there

a moment in silence;

Then he had turned away, and said: "I will

not awake him;

Let him sleep on,

it is best; for

what is the use of

more talking!"

Then he extin-

guished the light,

and threw him-

self down on his

pallet, 50

Dressed as he was, and ready to start at the
    break of the morning,—
Covered himself with the cloak he had worn
    in his campaigns in Flanders,—
Slept as a soldier sleeps in his bivouac, ready
    for action.
But with the dawn he arose; in the twilight
    Alden beheld him
Put on his corslet of steel, and all the rest of
    his armor,   55
Buckle about his waist his trusty blade of
    Damascus,
Take from the corner his musket, and so
    stride out of the chamber.
Often the heart of the youth had burned and
    yearned to embrace him,

Often his lips had essayed to speak, implor-
    ing for pardon;

All the old friendship came back, with its ten-
    der and grateful emotions; 60

But his pride overmastered the nobler nature
    within him,—

Pride, and the sense of his wrong, and the
    burning fire of the insult.

So he beheld his friend departing in anger,
    but spake not,

Saw him go forth to danger, perhaps to
    death, and he spake not!

Then he arose from his bed, and heard what
    the people were saying, 65

Joined in tne talk at the door, with Stephen
    and Richard and Gilbert,

Joined in the morning prayer, and in the
  reading of Scripture,
And, with the others, in haste went hurrying
  down to the sea-shore,
Down to the Plymouth Rock, that had been
  to their feet as a door-step
Into a world unknown,—the corner-stone of
  a nation!   70

MONUMENT NOW GUARDING THE PLYMOUTH ROCK.

There with his boat was the Master, already a little impatient

Lest he should lose the tide, or the wind
might shift to the eastward,

Square-built, hearty, and strong, with an
odor of ocean about him,

Speaking with this one and that, and cram-
ming letters and parcels

Into his pockets capacious, and messages
mingled together   75

Into his narrow brain, till at last he was
wholly bewildered.

Nearer the boat stood Alden, with one foot
placed on the gunwale,

One still firm on the rock, and talking at
times with the sailors,

Seated erect on the thwarts, all ready and
  eager for starting.

He too was eager to go, and thus put an end
  to his anguish,   80

Thinking to fly from despair, that swifter
  than keel is or canvas,

Thinking to drown in the sea the ghost that
  would rise and pursue him.

But as he gazed on the crowd, he beheld the
  form of Priscilla

Standing dejected among them, unconscious
  of all that was passing.

Fixed were her eyes upon his, as if she divined his intention,   85

Fixed with a look so sad, so reproachful, im-
  ploring, and patient,

That with a sudden revulsion his heart re-
coiled from its purpose,

As from the verge of a crag, where one step
more is destruction.

Strange is the heart of man, with its quick,
mysterious instincts!

Strange is the life of man, and fatal or fated
are moments, 90

Whereupon turn, as on hinges, the gates of
the wall adamantine!

"Here I remain!" he exclaimed, as he looked
at the heavens above him,

Thanking the Lord whose breath had scat-
tered the mist and the madness,

Wherein, blind and lost, to death he was
staggering headlong.

"Yonder snow-white cloud, that floats in the
    ether above me,   95
Seems like a hand that is pointing and beck-
    oning over the ocean.
There is another hand, that is not so spectral
    and ghost-like,
Holding me, drawing me back, and clasping
    mine for protection.
Float, O hand of cloud, and vanish away in
    the ether!
Roll thyself up like a fist, to threaten and
    daunt me; I heed not   100
Either your warning or menace, or any omen
    of evil!
There is no land so sacred, no air so pure and
    so wholesome,

As is the air she breathes, and the soil that is

    pressed by her footsteps.

Here for her sake will I stay, and like an in-

    visible presence

Hover around her for ever, protecting, sup-

    porting her weakness;   105

Yes! as my foot was the first that stepped on

    this rock at the landing,

So, with the blessing of God, shall it be the

    last at the leaving!"

Meanwhile the Master alert, but with dig-

    nified air and important,

Scanning with watchful eye the tide and the

    wind and the weather,

Walked about on the sands; and the people
crowded around him   110
Saying a few last words, and enforcing his
careful remembrance.
Then, taking each by the hand, as if he were
grasping a tiller,
Into the boat he sprang, and in haste shoved
off to his vessel,
Glad in his heart to get rid of all this worry
and flurry,
Glad to be gone from a land of sand and sick-
ness and sorrow,   115
Short allowance of victual, and plenty of
nothing but Gospel!
Lost in the sound of the oars was the last
farewell of the Pilgrims.

O strong hearts and true! not one went back

    in the May Flower!

No, not one looked back, who had set his

    hand to this ploughing!

Soon were heard on board the shouts and

    songs of the sailors   **120**

Heaving the windlass round, and hoisting

    the ponderous anchor.

Then the yards were braced, and all sails set

    to the west-wind,

Blowing steady and strong; and the May
    Flower sailed from the harbor,
Rounded the point of the Gurnet, and leav-
    ing far to the southward
Island and cape of sand, and the Field of the
    First Encounter,   125
Took the wind on her quarter, and stood for
    the open Atlantic,
Borne on the sand of the sea, and the swell-
    ing hearts of the Pilgrims.

Long in silence they watched the receding
    sail of the vessel,
Much endeared to them all, as something liv-
    ing and human;

Then, as if filled with the spirit, and wrapt in
    a vision prophetic, 130
Baring his hoary head, the excellent Elder of
    Plymouth
Said, "Let us pray!" and they prayed, and
    thanked the Lord and took courage.
Mournfully sobbed the waves at the base of
    the rock, and above them
Bowed and whispered the wheat on the hill
    of death, and their kindred
Seemed to awake in their graves, and to join
    in the prayer that they uttered. 135
Sun-illumined and white, on the eastern
    verge of the ocean
Gleamed the departing sail, like a marble slab
    in a graveyard;

Buried beneath it lay for ever all hope of es-
    caping.

Lo! as they turned to depart, they saw the
    form of an Indian,

Watching them from the hill; but while they
    spake with each other,   140

Pointing with outstretched hands, and say-
    ing, "Look!" he had vanished.

So they returned to their homes; but Alden
    lingered a little,

Musing alone on the shore, and watching the
    wash of the billows

Round the base of the rock, and the sparkle
    and flash of the sunshine,

Like the spirit of God, moving visibly over
    the waters.   145

VI.

PRISCILLA.

HUS for a while he
stood, and mused
by the shore of
the ocean,
Thinking of many
things, and most
of all of Priscilla;
And as if thought had the power to draw to
itself, like the loadstone,

Whatsoever it touches, by subtile laws of its
    nature,
Lo! as he turned to depart, Priscilla was
    standing beside him.   5

"Are you so much offended, you will not
    speak to me?" said she.
"Am I so much to blame, that yesterday,
    when you were pleading
Warmly the cause of another, my heart, im-
    pulsive and wayward,
Pleaded your own, and spake out, forgetful
    perhaps of decorum?
Certainly you can forgive me for speaking so
    frankly, for saying   10

What I ought not to have said, yet now I can
    never unsay it;
For there are moments in life, when the
    heart is so full of emotion,
That if by chance it be shaken, or into its
    depths like a pebble
Drops some careless word, it overflows, and
    its secret,
Spilt on the ground like water, can never be
    gathered together.   15
Yesterday I was shocked, when I heard you
    speak of Miles Standish,
Praising his virtues, transforming his **very**
    defects into virtues,

Praising his cour-
age and strength,
and even his
fighting in Fland-
ers,

As if by fighting alone you could win the

heart of a woman,

Quite overlooking yourself and the rest, in

exalting your hero.   20

Therefore I spake as I did, by an irresistible

impulse.

You will forgive me, I hope, for the sake of

the friendship between us,

Which is too true and too sacred to be so

easily broken!"

Thereupon answered John Alden, the schol-
    ar, the friend of Miles Standish:

"I was not angry with you, with myself alone
    I was angry,   25

Seeing how badly I managed the matter I
    had in my keeping."

"No!" interrupted the maiden, with answer
    prompt and decisive;

"No; you were angry with me, for speaking
    so frankly and freely.

It was wrong, I acknowledge; for it is the
    fate of a woman

Long to be patient and silent, to wait like a
    ghost that is speechless,   30

Till some questioning voice dissolves the
    spell of its silence.

Hence is the inner life of so many suffering
women

Sunless and silent and deep, like subterran-
ean rivers

Running through caverns of darkness, un-
heard, unseen, and unfruitful,

Chafing their channels of stone, with endless
and profitless murmurs."   35

Thereupon answered John Alden, the young
man, the lover of women:

"Heaven forbid it, Priscilla; and truly they
seem to me always

More like the beautiful rivers that watered
the garden of Eden,

More like the river Euphrates, through des-
erts of Havilah flowing,

Filling the land with delight, and memories

    sweet of the garden!"   40

"Ah, by these words, I can see," again inter-

    rupted the maiden,

"How very little you prize me, or care for

    what I am saying.

When from the depths of my heart, in pain

    and with secret misgiving,

Frankly I speak to you, asking for sympathy

    only and kindness,

Straightway you take up my words, that are

    plain and direct and in earnest,   45

Turn them away from their meaning, and

    answer with flattering phrases.

This is not right, is not just, is not true to

    the best that is in you;

For I know and esteem you, and feel that
        your nature is noble,

Lifting mine up to a higher, a more ethereal
        level.

Therefore I value your friendship, and feel it
        perhaps the more keenly

If you say aught that implies I am only as
        one among many,

If you make use of those common and com-
        plimentary phrases

Most men think so fine, in dealing and speak-
        ing with women,

But which women reject as insipid, if not as
        insulting."

Mute and amazed was Alden; and listened
and looked at Priscilla,   55
Thinking he never had seen her more fair,
more divine in her beauty.
He who but yesterday pleaded so glibly the
cause of another,
Stood there embarrassed and silent, and
seeking in vain for an answer.
So the maiden went on, and little divined or
imagined
What was at work in his heart, that made
him so awkward and speechless.   60
"Let us, then, be what we are, and speak
what we think, and in all things
Keep ourselves loyal to truth, and the sacred
professions of friendship.

It is no secret I tell you, nor am I ashamed to
  declare it:
I have liked to be with you, to see you, to
  speak with you always.
So I was hurt at your words, and a little af-
  fronted to hear you   65
Urge me to marry your friend, though he
  were the Captain Miles Standish.
For I must tell you the truth: much more to
  me is your friendship
Than all the love he could give, were he twice
  the hero you think him."
Then she extended her hand, and Alden, who
  eagerly grasped it,
Felt all the wounds in his heart, that were
  aching and bleeding so sorely,   70

Healed by the touch of that hand, and he
said, with a voice full of feeling:
"Yes, we must ever be friends; and of all
who offer you friendship
Let me be ever the first, the truest, the near-
est and dearest!"

Casting a farewell look at the glimmering
sail of the May Flower,
Distant, but still in sight, and sinking below
the horizon,   75
Homeward together they walked, with a
strange, indefinite feeling,
That all the rest had departed and left them
alone in the desert.

But, as they went through the fields in the
   blessing and smile of the sunshine,
Lighter grew their hearts, and Priscilla said
   very archly:
"Now that our terrible Captain has gone in
   pursuit of the Indians,   80
Where he is happier far than he would be
   commanding a household,
You may speak boldly, and tell me of all that
   happened between you,
When you returned last night, and said how
   ungrateful you found me."
Thereupon answered John Alden, and told
   her the whole of the story,—
Told her his own despair, and the direful
   wrath of Miles Standish.   85

Whereat the maiden smiled, and said between laughing and earnest,

"He is a little chimney, and heated hot in a
moment!"

But as he gently rebuked her, and told her
how much he had suffered,—

How he had even determined to sail that day
in the May Flower,

And had remained for her sake, on hearing
the dangers that threatened,—   90

All her manner was changed, and she said
with a faltering accent,

"Truly I thank you for this: how good you
have been to me always!"

Thus, as a pilgrim devout, who toward Je-
  rusalem journeys,
Taking three steps in advance, and one reluc-
  tantly backward,
Urged by importunate zeal, and withheld by
  pangs of contrition;   IOC
Slowly but steadily onward, receding yet
  ever advancing,
Journeyed this Puritan youth to the Holy
  Land of his longings,
Urged by the fervor of love, and withheld by
  remorseful misgivings.

VII.

THE MARCH OF MILES STANDISH.

EANWHILE the stalwart Miles Standish was marching steadily northward,

Winding through forest and swamp, and along the trend of the seashore,

All day long, with hardly a halt, the fire of his anger

Burning and crackling within, and the sulphurous odor of powder

Seeming more
sweet to his nos-
trils than all the
scents of the for-
est.   5
Silent and moody
he went, and
much he revolved
his discomfort;
He who was used to
success, and to
easy victories al-
ways,
Thus to be flouted,
rejected, and
laughed to scorn
by a maiden,

Thus to be mocked and betrayed by the friend
whom most he had trusted!
Ah! 'twas too much to be borne, and he fret-
ted and chafed in his armor!   10

"I alone am to blame," he muttered, "for
mine was the folly.
What has a rough old soldier, grown grim
and gray in the harness,
Used to the camp and its ways, to do with
the wooing of maidens?
'Twas but a dream,—let it pass,—let it vanish like so many others!
What I thought was a flower, is only a weed,
and is worthless;   15

Out of my heart will I pluck it, and throw it
    away, and henceforward

Be but a fighter of battles, a lover and wooer
    of dangers!"

Thus he revolved in his mind his sorry de-
    feat and discomfort,

While he was marching by day or lying at
    night in the forest,

Looking up at the trees, and the constella-
    tions beyond them.

2C

    After a three days'
        march he came to
        a n Indian e n-
        campment

    Pitched on the edge
        of a meadow, be-
        tween the sea and
        the forest;

Women at work by the tents, and the warriors, horrid with war-paint,

Seated about a fire, and smoking and talking
 together;

Who, when they saw from afar the sudden
 approach of the white men,   25

Saw the flash of the sun on breastplate and
 sabre and musket,

Straightway leaped to their feet, and two,
 from among them advancing,

Came to parley with Standish, and offer him
 furs as a present;

Friendship was in their looks, but in their
 hearts there was hatred.

Braves of the tribe were these, and brothers
 gigantic in stature,   30

Huge as Goliath of Gath, or the terrible Og,

king of Bashan;

One was Pecksuot named, and the other was

called Wattawamat.

Round their necks were suspended their

knives in scabbards of wampum,

Two-edged, trenchant knives, with points as

sharp as a needle.

Other arms had they none, for they were

cunning and crafty. 35

"Welcome, English!" they said,—these

words they had learned from the

traders

Touching at times on the coast, to barter

and chaffer for peltries.

Then in their native tongue they began to
    parley with Standish,
Through his guide and interpreter, Hobo-
    mok, friend of the white man,

After a three days' march he came to an Indian encampment
Pitched on the edge of a meadow, between the sea and the forest.

Begging for blankets and knives, but mostly
    for muskets and powder,   40

Kept by the white man, they said, concealed,
     with the plague, in his cellars,

Ready to be let loose, and destroy his brother
     the red man!

But when Standish refused, and said he
     would give them the Bible,

Suddenly changing their tone, they began to
     boast and to bluster.

Then Wattawamat advanced with a stride in
     front of the other,   45

And, with a lofty demeanor, thus vauntingly
     spake to the Captain:

"Now Wattawamat can see, by the fiery eyes
     of the Captain,

Angry is he in his heart; but the heart of
     the brave Wattawamat

Is not afraid at the sight.   He was not born
    of a woman,

But on a mountain, at night, from an oak-
    tree riven by lightning,   50

Forth he sprang at a bound, with all his
    weapons about him,

Shouting, 'Who is there here to fight with
    the brave Wattawamat?' "

Then he unsheathed his knife, and, whetting
    the blade on his left hand,

Held it aloft and displayed a woman's face
    on the handle,

Saying, with bitter expression and look of
    sinister meaning: 55

"I have another at home, with the face of a
    man on the handle;

By and by they shall marry; and there will
    be plenty of children!"

Then stood Pecksuot forth self-vaunting,
    insulting Miles Standish:
While with his fingers he patted the knife
    that hung at his bosom,
Drawing it half from its sheath, and plung-
    ing it back, as he muttered,   60

        "By and by it shall
          see; it shall eat;
          ah, ha! but shall
          speak not!
        This is the mighty
Captain the white men have sent to de-
    stroy us!

He is a little man; let him go and work with
the women!"

Meanwhile Standish had noted the faces
and figures of Indians

Peeping and creeping about from bush to
tree in the forest,   65

Feigning to look for game, with arrows set
on their bow-strings,

Drawing about him still closer and closer the
net of their ambush.

But undaunted he stood, and dissembled and
treated them smoothly;

So the old chronicles say, that were writ in
the days of the fathers.

But when he heard their defiance, the boast,
the taunt, and the insult,   70
All the hot blood of his race, of Sir Hugh
and of Thurston de Standish,
Boiled and beat in his heart, and swelled in
the veins of his temples.
Headlong he leaped on the boaster, and,
snatching his knife from its scabbard,
Plunged it into his heart, and, reeling backward, the savage
Fell with his face to the sky, and a fiendlike
fierceness upon it.   75
Straight there arose from the forest the awful
sound of the war-whoop,
And, like a flurry of snow on the whistling
wind of December,

Swift and sudden and keen came a flight of
  feathery arrows.

Then came a cloud of smoke, and out of the
  cloud came the lightning,

Out of the lightning thunder; and death unseen ran before it.   80

Frightened the savages fled for shelter in
  swamp and in thicket,

Hotly pursued and beset; but their sachem,
  the brave Wattawamat,

Fled not; he was dead. Unswerving and
  swift had a bullet

Passed through his brain, and he fell with
  both hands clutching the greensward,

Seeming in death to hold back from his foe
  the land of his fathers.   85

There on the flowers of the meadow the
warriors lay, and above them,
Silent, with folded arms, stood Hobomok,
friend of the white man.
Smiling at length he exclaimed to the stalwart Captain of Plymouth:
"Pecksuot bragged very loud, of his courage,
his strength, and his stature,—
Mocked the great Captain, and called him a
little man; but I see now   90
Big enough have you been to lay him speechless before you!"

Thus the first battle was fought and won
by the stalwart Miles Standish.

When the tidings thereof were brought to the
> village of Plymouth,

And as a trophy of war the head of the brave
> Wattawamat

Scowled from the roof of the fort, which at
> once was a church and a fortress,   95

All who beheld it rejoiced, and praised the
> Lord, and took courage.

Only Priscilla averted her face from this
> spectre of terror,

Thanking God in her heart that she had not
> married Miles Standish;

Shrinking, fearing almost, lest, coming home
> from his battles,

He should lay claim to her hand, as the prize
> and reward of his valor.   100

VIII.

THE SPINNING WHEEL.

ONTH after month
passed away, and
in Autumn the
ships of the mer-
chants

Came with kindred and friends, with cattle
and corn for the Pilgrims.

All in the village was peace; the men were
intent on their labors,

Busy with hewing and building, with garden-
plot and with merestead,
Busy with breaking the glebe, and mowing
the grass in the meadows,   **5**
Searching the sea for its fish, and hunting the
deer in the forest.
All in the village was peace; but at times the
rumor of warfare
Filled the air with alarm, and the apprehen-
sion of danger.
Bravely the stalwart Miles Standish was
scouring the land with his forces,
Waxing valiant in fight and defeating the
alien armies,   **10**
Till his name had become a sound of fear to
the nations.

Anger was still in his heart, but at times the
    remorse and contrition
Which in all noble natures succeed the pas-
    sionate outbreak,
Came like a rising tide, that encounters the
    rush of a river,
Staying its current awhile, but making it bit-
    ter and brackish.   15

Meanwhile Alden at home had built him a
                    n e w   habitation,
                    Solid,   substantial,
                    of timber rough-
                    hewn   from   the
                    firs of the forest.

Wooden-barred was the door, and the roof

    was covered with rushes;

Latticed the windows were, and the window-

    panes were of paper,

Oiled to admit the light, while wind and rain

    were excluded.   20

There too he dug a well, and around it plant-

    ed an orchard:

Still may be seen to this day some trace of

    the well and the orchard.

Close to the house was the stall, where, safe

    and secure from annoyance,

Raghorn, the snow-white steer, that had fall-

    en to Alden's allotment

In the division of cattle, might ruminate in

    the night-time   25

Over the pastures he cropped, made fragrant
    by sweet pennyroyal.

Oft when his labor was finished, with eag-
    er feet would the dreamer
Follow the pathway that ran through the
    woods to the house of Priscilla,
Led by illusions romantic and subtile decep-
    tions of fancy,
Pleasure disguised as duty, and love in the
    semblance of friendship.   30
Ever of her he thought, when he fashioned
    the walls of his dwelling;
Ever of her he thought, when he delved in
    the soil of his garden;

Ever of her he thought, when he read in his
    Bible on Sunday
Praise of the virtuous woman, as she is de-
    scribed in the Proverbs,—
How the heart of her husband doth safely
    trust in her always,   35
How all the days of her life she will do him
    good, and not evil,
How she seeketh the wool and the flax and
    worketh with gladness,
How she layeth her hand to the spindle and
    holdeth the distaff,
How she is not afraid of the snow for herself
    or her household,
Knowing her household are clothed with the
    scarlet cloth of her weaving!   40

So as she sat at her wheel one afternoon in
Autumn,

Alden, who opposite
sa t, a n d w a s
w a t c h i n g her
dexterous fingers,
As if the thread she
was s p i n n i n g
were that of his life and his fortune,
After a pause in their talk, thus spake to the
sound of the spindle.
"Truly, Priscilla," he said, "when I see you
spinning and spinning,
Never idle a moment, but thrifty and
thoughtful of others,

45

Suddenly you are transformed, are visibly
   changed in a moment;
You are no longer Priscilla, but Bertha the
   Beautiful Spinner."
Here the light foot on the treadle grew swift-
   er and swifter; the spindle
Uttered an angry snarl, and the thread
   snapped short in her fingers;   50
While the impetuous speaker, not heeding the
   mischief, continued:
"You are the beautiful Bertha, the spinner,
   the queen of Helvetia;
She whose story I read at a stall in the streets
   of Southampton,
Who, as she rode on her palfrey, o'er valley
   and meadow and mountain,

Ever was spinning her thread from a distaff
    fixed to her saddle.   55

She was so thrifty and good, that her name
    passed into a proverb.

So shall it be with your own, when the spin-
    ning-wheel shall no longer

Hum in the house of the farmer, and fill its
    chambers with music.

Then shall the mothers, reproving, relate how
    it was in their childhood,

Praising the good old times, and the days of
    Priscilla the spinner!"   60

Straight uprose from her wheel the beautiful
    Puritan maiden,

Pleased with the praise of her thrift from him
    whose praise was the sweetest,

Drew from the reel on the table a snowy
    skein of her spinning,

Thus making answer, meanwhile, to the flat-
    tering phrases of Alden:

"Come, you must not be idle; if I am a
    pattern for housewives,   65

Show yourself equally worthy of being the
    model of husbands.

Hold this skein on your hands, while I wind
    it, ready for knitting;

Then who knows but hereafter, when fash-
    ions have changed and the manners,

Fathers may talk to their sons of the good old
    time of John Alden!"

Thus, with a jest and a laugh, the skein on
    his hands she adjusted,   70

He sitting awkwardly there, with his arms
    extended before him,
She standing graceful, erect, and winding
    the thread from his fingers,
Sometimes chiding a little his clumsy man-
    ner of holding,
Sometimes touching his hands, as she disen-
    tangled expertly
Twist or knot in the yarn, unawares—for
    how could she help it?—   75
Sending electrical thrills through every
    nerve in his body.

Lo! in the midst of this scene, a breathless
    messenger entered,
Bringing in hurry and heat the terrible news
    from the village.

Yes; Miles Standish was dead!—an Indian
    had brought them the tidings,—

Slain by a poisoned arrow, shot down in the
    front of the battle,   80

Into an ambush beguiled, cut off with the
    whole of his forces;

All the town would be burned, and all the
    people be murdered!

Such were the tidings of evil that burst on
    the hearts of the hearers.

Silent and statue-like stood Priscilla, her face
    looking backward

Still at the face of the speaker, her arms up-
    lifted in horror;   85

But John Alden, upstarting, as if the barb of
    the arrow

Piercing the heart of his friend had struck
  his own, and had sundered

Once and forever the bonds that held him
  bound as a captive,

Wild with excess of sensation, the awful delight of his freedom,

Mingled with pain and regret, unconscious
  of what he was doing,   90

Clasped, almost with a groan, the motionless
  form of Priscilla,

Pressing her close to his heart, as forever his
  own, and exclaiming:

"Those whom the Lord hath united, let no
  man put them asunder!"

Even as rivulets twain, from distant and
  separate sources,

Seeing each other afar, as they leap from the
  rocks, and pursuing   95

Each one its devious path, but drawing
  nearer and nearer,

Rush together at last, at their trysting-place
  in the forest;

So these lives that had run thus far in separate channels,

Coming in sight of each other, then swerving
  and flowing asunder,

Parted by barriers strong, but drawing
  nearer and nearer,   100

Rushed together at last, and one was lost in
  the other.

IX.

THE WEDDING DAY.

FORTH from the curtain of clouds, from the tent of purple and scarlet, Issued the sun, the great High-Priest, in his garments resplendent, Holiness unto the Lord, in letters of light, on his forehead,

Round the hem of his robe the golden bells and pomegranates.

Blessing the **world** he came, and **the** bars of vapor **be-**neath him 5

Gleamed like a grate of brass, and the seat at his feet was a laver!

This was the wedding m o r n of Priscilla the Puritan maiden.

Friends were assembled together; the Elder
and Magistrate also
Graced the scene with their presence, and
stood like the Law and the Gospel,
One with the sanction of earth and one with
the blessing of heaven.   10
Simple and brief was the wedding, as that of
Ruth and Boaz.
Softly the youth and the maiden repeated
the words of betrothal,
Taking each other for husband and wife in
the Magistrate's presence,
After the Puritan way, and the laudable cus-
tom of Holland.
Fervently then, and devoutly, the excellent
Elder of Plymouth   15

Prayed for the hearth and the home, that
were founded that day in affection,
Speaking of life and of death, and implor-
ing divine benedictions.

Lo! when the service was ended, a form
appeared on the threshold,
Clad in armor of steel, a sombre and sorrow-
ful figure!
Why does the bridegroom start and stare at
the strange apparition?   20
Why does the bride turn pale, and hide her
face on his shoulder?
Is it a phantom of air,—a bodiless, spectral
illusion?

Is it a ghost from the grave, that has come

to forbid the betrothal?

Long had it stood there unseen, a guest un-

invited, unwelcomed;

Over its clouded eyes there had passed at

times an expression   25

Softening the gloom and revealing the warm

heart hidden beneath them,

As when across the sky the driving rack of

the rain-cloud

Grows for a moment thin, and betrays the

sun by its brightness.

Once it had lifted its hand, and moved its

lips, but was silent,

As if an iron will had mastered the fleeting

intention.   30

But when were ended the troth and the
prayer and the last benediction,
Into the room it strode, and the people beheld
with amazement
Bodily there in his armor Miles Standish, the
Captain of Plymouth!
Grasping the bridegroom's hand, he said with
emotion, "Forgive me!
I have been angry and hurt,—too long have
I cherished the feeling;   35
I have been cruel and hard, but now, thank
God! it is ended.
Mine is the same hot blood that leaped in the
veins of Hugh Standish,
Sensitive, swift to resent, but as swift in
atoning for error.

Never so much as now was Miles Standish
    the friend of John Alden."

Thereupon answered the bridegroom: "Let
    all be forgotten between us,—   40

All save the dear, old friendship, and that
    shall grow older and dearer!"

Then the Captain advanced, and, bowing,
    saluted Priscilla,

Gravely, and after the manner of old-fash-
    ioned gentry in England,

Something of camp and of court, of town
    and of country, commingled,

Wishing her joy of her wedding, and loudly
    lauding her husband.   45

Then he said with a smile: "I should have
    remembered the adage,—

If you would be well served, you must serve
  yourself; and moreover,
No man can gather cherries in Kent at the
  season of Christmas!"

Great was the people's amazement, and
  greater yet their rejoicing,
Thus to behold once more the sun-burnt face
  of their Captain,   50
Whom they had mourned as dead; and they
  gathered and crowded about him,
Eager to see him and hear him, forgetful of
  bride and of bridegroom,
Questioning, answering, laughing, and each
  interrupting the other,

Till the good Captain declared, being quite
      overpowered and bewildered,

He had rather by far break into an Indian
      encampment,   55

Than come again to a wedding to which he
      had not been invited.

Meanwhile the bridegroom went forth and
      stood with the bride at the doorway,

Breathing the perfumed air of that warm and
      beautiful morning.

Touched with autumnal tints, but lonely
      and sad in the sunshine,

Lay extended before them the land of toil
      and privation;   60

There were the graves of the dead, and the
    barren waste of the sea-shore,
There the familiar fields, the groves of pine,
    and the meadows;
But to their eyes transfigured, it seemed as
    the Garden of Eden,
Filled with the presence of God, whose voice
    was the sound of the ocean.

Soon was their vision disturbed by the
    noise and stir of departure,   65
Friends coming forth from the house, and
    impatient of longer delaying,
Each with his plan for the day, and the work
    that was left uncompleted.

Then from a stall near at hand, amid ex-
    clamations of wonder,

Alden the thoughtful, the careful, so happy,
    so proud of Priscilla,

Brought out his snow-white steer, obeying
    the hand of its master,   70

Led by a cord that was tied to an iron ring
    in its nostrils,

Covered with crimson cloth, and a cushion
    placed for a saddle.

She should not walk he said, through the
    dust and heat of the noonday;

Nay, she should ride like a queen, not plod
    along like a peasant.

Somewhat alarmed at first, but reassured by
    the others,   75

Placing her hand on the cushion, her foot in
the hand of her husband,

Gayly, with joyous laugh, Priscilla mounted
her palfrey.

"Nothing is wanting now," he said with a
smile, "but the distaff;

Then you would be in truth my queen, my
beautiful Bertha!"

Onward the bridal procession now moved
to their new habitation,   80

Happy husband and wife, and friends con-
    versing together.
Pleasantly murmured the brook, as they
    crossed the ford in the forest,
Pleased with the image that passed, like a
    dream of love through its bosom,
Tremulous, floating in air, o'er the depths of
    the azure abysses.
Down through the golden leaves the sun was
    pouring his splendors,

85

Gleaming on purple grapes, that, from
    branches above them suspended,
Mingled their odorous breath with the balm
    of the pine and the fir-tree,
Wild and sweet as the clusters that grew in
    the valley of Eshcol.

Like a picture it seemed of the primitive,
    pastoral ages,

Fresh with the youth of the world, and re-
    calling Rebecca and Isaac,   90

Old and yet ever new, and simple and beau-
    tiful always,

Love immortal and young in the endless suc-
    cession of lovers.

So through the Plymouth woods passed on-
    ward the bridal procession.

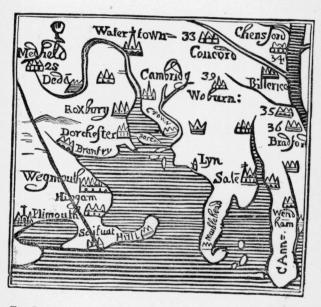

THE EARLIEST MAP OF BOSTON BAY AND THE SETTLEMENTS OF
THE PILGRIMS. DIRECTION NORTH IS TOWARD
THE RIGHT HAND.

IMPORTANT NOTICE.

The previous page completes the title volume of this book. The publishers include the following extra pages, not pertinent to the title, in order to make a book of sufficient thickness to conform with the series in which this book is published.

PROMETHEUS.

PROMETHEUS,

OR THE POET'S FORETHOUGHT.

OF Prometheus, how undaunted
  On Olympus' shining bastions
His audacious foot he planted,
Myths are told and songs are chaunted,
  Full of promptings and suggestions.

Beautiful is the tradition
  Of that flight through heavenly portals,
The old classic superstition
Of the theft and the transmission
  Of the fire of the Immortals!

First the deed of noble daring,
  Born of heavenward aspiration,

Then the fire with mortals sharing,
Then the vulture,—the despairing
  Cry of pain on crags of Caucasian.

All is but a symbol painted
  Of the Poet, Prophet, Seer;
Only those are crowned and sainted
Who with grief have been acquainted.
  Making nations nobler, freer.

In their feverish exultations,
  In their triumph and their yearnings,
In their passionate pulsations,
In their words among the nations,
  The Promethean fire is burning.

Shall it, then, be unavailing,
  All this toil for human culture?
Through the cloud-rack, dark and trailing,
Must they see above them sailing
  O'er life's barren crags the vulture?

Such a fate as this was Dante's,
　By defeat and exile maddened;
Thus were Milton and Cervantes,
Nature's priests and Corybantes,
　By affliction touched and saddened.

But the glories so transcendent
　That around their memories cluster,
And, on all their steps attendant,
Make their darkened lives resplendent
　With such gleams of inward lustre!

All the melodies mysterious,
　Through the dreary darkness chaunted;
Thoughts in attitudes imperious,
Voices soft, and deep, and serious,
　Words that whispered, songs that haunted!

All the soul in rapt suspension,
　All the quivering, palpitating

Chords of life in utmost tension,
With the fervor of invention,
  With the rapture of creating!

Ah, Prometheus! heaven-scaling!
  In such hours of exultation
Even the faintest heart, unquailing,
Might behold the vulture sailing
  Round the cloudy crags Caucasian!

Though to all there is not given
  Strength for such sublime endeavor,
Thus to scale the walls of heaven,
And to leaven with fiery leaven
  All the hearts of men for ever;

Yet all bards, whose hearts unblighted
  Honor and believe the presage,
Hold aloft their torches lighted,
Gleaming through the realms benighted,
  As they onward bear the message!

THE LADDER OF ST. AUGUSTINE.

SAINT AUGUSTINE! well hast thou said,
   That of our vices we can frame
A ladder, if we will but tread
   Beneath our feet each deed of shame!

All common things, each day's events,
   That with the hour begin and end,
Our pleasures and our discontents,
   Are rounds by which we may ascend.

The low desire, the base design,
    That makes another's virtues less;
The revel of the ruddy wine,
    And all occasions of excess;

The longing for ignoble things;
    The strife for triumph more than truth,
The hardening of the heart, that brings
    Irreverence for the dreams of youth;

All thoughts of ill; all evil deeds,
    That have their roots in thoughts of ill;
Whatever hinders or impedes
    The action of the nobler will :—

All these must first be trampled down
    Beneath our feet, if we would gain
In the bright fields of fair renown
    The right of eminent domain.

We have not wings, we cannot soar;
    But we have feet to scale and climb
By slow degrees, by more and more,
    The cloudy summits of our time.

The mighty pyramids of stone
    That wedge-like cleave the desert airs,
When nearer seen, and better known,
    Are but gigantic flights of stairs.

The distant mountains, that uprear
    Their solid bastions to the skies,
Are crossed by pathways, that appear
    As we to higher levels rise.

The heights by great men reached and kept
    Were not attained by sudden flight,
But they, while their companions slept,
    Were toiling upward in the night.

Standing on what too long we bore
  With shoulders bent and downcast eyes,
We may discern—unseen before—
  A pathway to higher destinies.

Nor deem the irrevocable Past,
  As wholly wasted, wholly vain,
If, rising on its wrecks, at last
  To something nobler we attain.

THE PHANTOM SHIP.

In Mather's Magnalia Christi,
  Of the old colonial time,
May be found in prose the legend
  That is here set down in rhyme.

A ship sailed from New Haven,
  And the keen and frosty airs,
That filled her sails at parting,
  Were heavy with good men's prayers.

"O Lord! if it be thy pleasure"—
    Thus prayed the old divine—
"To bury our friends in the ocean,
    Take them, for they are thine!"

But Master Lamberton muttered,
    And under his breath said he,
"This ship is so crank and walty
    I fear our grave she will be!"

And the ships that came from England,
    When the winter months were gone,
Brought no tidings of this vessel
Nor of Master Lamberton.

This put the people to praying
    That the Lord would let them hear
What in his greater wisdom
    He had done with friends so dear.

And at last their prayers were answered :—
   It was in the month of June,
An hour before the sunset
   Of a windy afternoon,

When, steadily steering landward,
   A ship was seen below,
And they knew it was Lamberton, Master,
   Who sailed so long ago.

On she came, with a cloud of canvas,
   Right against the wind that blew,
Until the eye could distinguish
   The faces of the crew.

Then fell her straining topmasts,
   Hanging tangled in the shrouds,
And her sails were loosened and lifted,
   And blown away like clouds.

And the masts, with all their rigging,
  Fell slowly, one by one,
And the hulk dilated and vanished,
  As a sea-mist in the sun!

And the people who saw this marvel
  Each said unto his friend,
That this was the mould of their vessel,
  And thus her tragic end.

And the pastor of the village
  Gave thanks to God in prayer,
That, to quiet their troubled spirits,
  He had sent his Ship of Air.

THE WARDEN OF THE CINQUE PORTS.

A MIST was driving down the British Channel,
  The day was just begun,
And through the window-panes, on floor and
        panel,
  Streamed the red autumn sun.

It glanced on flowing flag and rippling pennon,
  And the white sails of ships;
And, from the frowning rampart, the black can-
    non
  Hailed it with feverish lips.

169

Sandwich and Romney, Hastings, Hithe, and
      Dover
   Were all alert that day,
To see the French war-steamers speeding over,
   When the fog cleared away.

Sullen and silent, and like couchant lions,
   Their cannon, through the night,
Holding their breath, had watched, in grim de-
      fiance,
   The sea-coast opposite.

And now they roared at drum-beat from their
      stations
   On every citadel;
Each answering each, with morning salutations,
   That all was well.

And down the coast, all taking up the burden,
    Replied the distant forts,
As if to summon from his sleep the Warden
    And Lord of the Cinque Ports.

Him shall no sunshine from the fields of azure,
    No drum-beat from the wall,
No morning gun from the black fort's embrasure,
    Awaken with its call!

No more, surveying with an eye impartial
    The long line of the coast,
Shall the gaunt figure of the old Field Marshal
    Be seen upon his post!

For in the night, unseen, a single warrior,
    In sombre harness mailed,
Dreaded of man, and surnamed the Destroyer,
    The rampart wall has scaled.

He passed into the chamber of the sleeper,
   The dark and silent room,
And as he entered, darker grew, and deeper,
   The silence and the gloom.

He did not pause to parley or dissemble,
   But smote the Warden hoar;
Ah! what a blow! that made all England tremble
   And groan from shore to shore.

Meanwhile, without, the surly cannon waited,
   The sun rose bright o'erhead;
Nothing in Nature's aspect intimated
   That a great man was dead.

HAUNTED HOUSES.

———

ALL houses wherein men have lived and died
    Are haunted houses. Through the open doors
The harmless phantoms on their errands glide,
    With feet that make no sound upon the floors.

We meet them at the door-way, on the stair,
    Along the passages they come and go,
Impalpable impressions on the air,
    A sense of something moving to and fro.

There are more guests at table than the hosts
    Invited; the illuminated hall
Is thronged with quiet, inoffensive ghosts,
    As silent as the pictures on the wall.

The stranger at my fireside cannot see
    The forms I see, nor hear the sounds I hear;
He but perceives what is; while unto me
    All that has been is visible and clear.

We have no title-deeds to house or lands;
    Owners and occupants of earlier dates
From graves forgotten stretch their dusty hands,
    And hold in mortmain still their old estates.

The spirit-world around this world of sense
    Floats like an atmosphere, and everywhere
Wafts through these earthly mists and vapors
      dense
    A vital breath of more ethereal air.

Our little lives are kept in equipoise
   By opposite attractions and desires;
The struggle of the instinct that enjoys,
   And the more noble instinct that aspires.

These perturbations, this perpetual jar
   Of earthly wants and aspirations high,
Come from the influence of an unseen star,
   An undiscovered planet in our sky.

And as the moon from some dark gate of cloud
   Throws o'er the sea a floating bridge of light,
Across whose trembling planks our fancies crowd
   Into the realm of mystery and night,—

So from the world of spirits there descends
   A bridge of light, connecting it with this,
O'er whose unsteady floor, that sways and bends,
   Wander our thoughts above the dark abyss.

IN THE CHURCHYARD AT CAMBRIDGE

— ⚬ —

In the village churchyard she lies,
Dust is in her beautiful eyes,
   No more she breathes, nor feels, nor stirs;
At her feet and at her head
Lies a slave to attend the dead,
   But their dust is white as hers.

Was she a lady of high degree,
So much in love with the vanity
   And foolish pomp of this world of ours?

176

Or was it Christian charity,
And lowliness and humility,
   The richest and rarest of all dowers?

Who shall tell us? No one speaks;
No color shoots into those cheeks,
   Either of anger or of pride,
At the rude question we have asked;
Nor will the mystery be unmasked
   By those who are sleeping at her side.

Hereafter?—And do you think to look
On the terrible pages of that Book
   To find her failings, faults, and errors?
Ah, you will then have other cares,
In your own short-comings and despairs,
   In your own secret sins and terrors!

THE EMPEROR'S BIRD'S-NEST.

Once the Emperor Charles of Spain,
   With his swarthy, grave commanders,
I forget in what campaign,
Long besieged, in mud and rain,
   Some old frontier town in Flanders.

Up and down the dreary camp,
   In great boots of Spanish leather,
Striding with a measured tramp,
These Hidalgos, dull and damp,
   Cursed the Frenchman, cursed the weather.

178

Thus as to and fro they went,
　　Over upland and through hollow,
Giving their impatience vent,
Perched upon the Emperor's tent,
　　In her nest, they spied a swallow.

Yes, it was a swallow's nest,
　　Built of clay and hair of horses,
Mane, or tail, or dragoon's crest,
Found on hedge-rows east and west,
　　After skirmish of the forces.

Then an old Hidalgo said,
　　As he twirled his gray mustachio,
"Sure this swallow overhead
Thinks the Emperor's tent a shed,
　　And the Emperor but a Macho!"

Hearing his imperial name
　　Coupled with those words of malice,

Half in anger, half in shame,
Forth the great campaigner came
  Slowly from his canvas palace.

"Let no hand the bird molest,"
  Said he solemnly, "nor hurt her!"
Adding then, by way of jest,
"Golondrina is my guest,
  'Tis the wife of some deserter!"

Swift as bowstring speeds a shaft,
  Through the camp was spread the rumor,
And the soldiers, as they quaffed
Flemish beer at dinner, laughed
  At the Emperor's pleasant humor.

So unharmed and unafraid
  Sat the swallow still and brooded,
Till the constant cannonade
Through the walls a breach had made,
  And the siege was thus concluded.

Then the army, elsewhere bent,
   Struck its tents as if disbanding,
Only not the Emperor's tent,
For he ordered, ere he went,
   Very curtly, "Leave it standing!"

So it stood there all alone,
   Loosely flapping, torn and tattered,
Till the brood was fledged and flown,
Singing o'er those walls of stone
   Which the cannon-shot had shattered.

THE TWO ANGELS.

Two angels, one of Life and one of Death,
　Passed o'er our village as the morning broke;
The dawn was on their faces, and beneath,
　　The sombre houses hearsed with plumes of
　　smoke.

Their attitude and aspect were the same,
　Alike their features and their robes of white;
But one was crowned with amaranth, as with
　　flame,
　　And one with asphodels, like flakes of light.

I saw them pause on their celestial way;
    Then said I, with deep fear and doubt op-
        pressed,
"Beat not so loud, my heart, lest thou betray
    The place where thy beloved are at rest!"

And he who wore the crown of asphodels,
    Descending at my door, began to knock,
And my soul sank within me, as in wells
    The waters sink before an earthquake's shock.

I recognized the nameless agony,
    The terror and the tremor and the pain,
That oft before had filled and haunted me,
    And now returned with threefold strength
        again.

The door I opened to my heavenly guest,
    And listened, for I thought I heard God's voice;

And, knowing whatsoe'er he sent was best,
   Dared neither to lament nor to rejoice.

Then with a smile, that filled the house with light,
   "My errand is not Death, but Life," he said;
And ere I answered, passing out of sight,
   On his celestial embassy he sped.

'T was at thy door, O friend! and not at mine,
   The angel with the amaranthine wreath,
Pausing, descended, and with voice divine,
   Whispered a word that had a sound like Death.

Then fell upon the house a sudden gloom,
   A shadow on those features fair and thin;
And softly, from that hushed and darkened room,
   Two angels issued, where but one went in.

All is of God!   If he but wave his hand,
   The mists collect, the rain falls thick and loud,
Till, with a smile of light on sea and land,
   Lo! he looks back from the departing cloud.

Angels of Life and Death alike are his;
   Without his leave they pass no threshold o'er;
Who, then, would wish or dare, believing this,
   Against his messengers to shut the door?

DAYLIGHT AND MOONLIGHT

In broad daylight, and at noon,
Yesterday I saw the moon
Sailing high, but faint and white,
As a school-boy's paper kite.

In broad daylight, yesterday,
I read a Poet's mystic lay;
And it seemed to me at most
As a phantom, or a ghost.

But at length the feverish day
Like a passion died away,
And the night, serene and still,
Fell on village, vale, and hill.

Then the moon, in all her pride,
Like a spirit glorified,
Filled and overflowed the night
With revelations of her light.

And the Poet's song again
Passed like music through my brain;
Night interpreted to me
All its grace and mystery.

THE JEWISH CEMETERY AT NEWPORT.

———

How strange it seems!   These Hebrews in their
    graves,
    Close by the street of this fair seaport town,
Silent beside the never-silent waves,
    At rest in all this moving up and down!

The trees are white with dust, that o'er their sleep
    Wave their broad curtains in the south wind's
        breath,
While underneath such leafy tents they keep
    The long, mysterious Exodus of Death.

And these sepulchral stones, so old and brown,
  That pave with level flags their burial-place,
Seem like the tablets of the Law, thrown down
  And broken by Moses at the mountain's base.

The very names recorded here are strange,
  Of foreign accent, and of different climes;
Alvares and Rivera interchange
  With Abraham and Jacob of old times.

"Blessed be God! for he created Death!"
  The mourners said, "and Death is rest and
      peace";
Then added, in the certainty of faith,
  "And giveth Life that never more shall cease."

Closed are the portals of their Synagogue,
  No Psalms of David now the silence break,

No Rabbi reads the ancient Decalogue
   In the grand dialect the Prophets spake.

Gone are the living, but the dead remain,
   And not neglected; for a hand unseen,
Scattering its bounty, like a summer rain,
   Still keeps their graves and their remembrance
      green.

How came they here? What burst of Christian
      hate,
   What persecution, merciless and blind,
Drove o'er the sea—that desert desolate—
   These Ishmaels and Hagars of mankind?

They lived in narrow streets and lanes obscure,
   Ghetto and Judenstrass, in mirk and mire;
Taught in the school of patience to endure
   The life of anguish and the death of fire.

All their lives long, with the unleavened bread
  And bitter herbs of exile and its fears,
The wasting famine of the heart they fed,
  And slaked its thirst with marah of their tears.

Anathema maranatha! was the cry
  That rang from town to town, from street to
    street;
At every gate the accursed Mordecai
  Was mocked and jeered, and spurned by Chris-
    tian feet.

Pride and humiliation hand in hand
  Walked with them through the world where'er
    they went;
Trampled and beaten were they as the sand,
  And yet unshaken as the continent.

For in the background figures vague and vast
  Of patriarchs and of prophets rose sublime,

And all the great traditions of the Past
  They saw reflected in the coming time.

And thus forever with reverted look
  The mystic volume of the world they read,
Spelling it backward, like a Hebrew book,
  Till life became a Legend of the Dead.

But ah! what once has been shall be no more!
  The groaning earth in travail and in pain
Brings forth its races, but does not restore,
  And the dead nations never rise again.

OLIVER BASSLLIN.

———

In the Valley of the Vire
  Still is seen an ancient mill,
With its gables quaint and queer,
  And beneath the window-sill,
    On the stone,
    These words alone:
"Oliver Basselin lived here."

Far above it, on the steep,
  Ruined stands the old Chateau·
Nothing but the donjon-keep
  Left for shelter or for show.

Its vacant eyes
Stare at the skies,
Stare at the valley green and deep.

Once a convent, old and brown,
    Looked, but ah! it looks no more,
From the neighboring hillside down
    On the rushing and the roar
        Of the stream
        Whose sunny gleam
Cheers the little Norman town.

In that darksome mill of stone,
    To the water's dash and din,
Careless, humble, and unknown,
    Sang the poet Basselin
        Songs that fill
        That ancient mill
With a splendor of its own.

Never feeling of unrest
　　Broke the pleasant dream he dreamed;
Only made to be his nest,
　　All the lovely valley seemed;
　　　　No desire
　　　　Of soaring higher
Stirred or fluttered in his breast.

True, his songs were not divine;
　　Were not songs of that high art,
Which, as winds do in the pine,
　　Find an answer in each heart;
　　　　But the mirth
　　　　Of this green earth
Laughed and reveled in his line.

From the alehouse and the inn,
　　Opening on the narrow street,
Came the loud, convivial din,
　　Singing and applause of feet,

　　　　The laughing lays
　　　　That in those days
　　Sang the poet Basselin.

In the castle, cased in steel,
　　Knights, who fought at Agincourt,
Watched and waited, spur on heel;
　　But the poet sang for sport
　　　　Songs that rang
　　　　Another clang,
Songs that lowlier hearts could feel.

In the convent, clad in gray,
　　Sat the monks in lonely cells,
Paced the cloisters, knelt to pray,
　　And the poet heard their bells;
　　　　But his rhymes
　　　　Found other chimes,
Nearer to the earth than they.

Gone are all the barons bold,
   Gone are all the knights and squires,
Gone the abbot stern and cold,
   And the brotherhood of friars;
       Not a name
       Remains to fame,
From those mouldering days of old!

But the poet's memory here
   Of the landscape makes a part;
Like the river, swift and clear,
   Flows his song through many a heart;
       Haunting still
       That ancient mill,
In the Valley of the Vire.

VICTOR GALBRAITH.

———

Under the walls of Monterey
At daybreak the bugles began to play,
     Victor Galbraith!
In the midst of the morning damp and gray,
These were the words they seemed to say:
     "Come forth to thy death,
     Victor Galbraith!"

Forth he came, with a martial tread;
Firm was his step, erect his head;
     Victor Galbraith,

198

He who so well the bugle played,
Could not mistake the words it said:
    "Come forth to thy death,
    Victor Galbraith!"

He looked at the earth, he looked at the sky,
He looked at the files of musketry,
    Victor Galbraith!
And he said, with a steady voice and eye,
"Take good aim; I am ready to die!"
    Thus challenges death
    Victor Galbraith.

Twelve fiery tongues flashed straight and red,
Six leaden balls on their errand sped;
    Victor Galbraith
Falls to the ground, but he is not dead;
His name was not stamped on those balls of lead,
    And they only scath
    Victor Galbraith.

Three balls are in his breast and brain,
But he rises out of the dust again,
　　　Victor Galbraith!
The water he drinks has a bloody stain;
"O kill me, and put me out of my pain!"
　　　In his agony prayeth
　　　Victor Galbraith.

Forth dart once more those tongues of flame,
And the bugler has died a death of shame,
　　　Victor Galbraith!
His soul has gone back to whence it came,
And no one answers to the name,
　　　When the Sergeant saith,
　　　"Victor Galbraith!"

Under the walls of Monterey
By night a bugle is heard to play,
　　　Victor Galbraith!

Through the mist of the valley damp and gray
The sentinels hear the sound, and say,

"That is the wraith
Of Victor Galbraith!"

MY LOST YOUTH.

Often I think of the beautiful town
   That is seated by the sea;
Often in thought go up and down
The pleasant streets of that dear old town,
   And my youth comes back to me.
     And a verse of a Lapland song
     Is haunting my memory still:
   "A boy's will is the wind's will,
And the thoughts of youth are long, long
     thoughts."

I can see the shadowy lines of its trees,
   And catch, in sudden gleams,
The sheen of the far-surrounding seas,
And islands that were the Hesperides
   Of all my boyish dreams.
      And the burden of that old song,
      It murmurs and whispers still:
   "A boy's will is the wind's will,
And the thoughts of youth are long, long
     thoughts."

I remember the black wharves and the slips,
   And the sea-tides tossing free;
And Spanish sailors with bearded lips,
And the beauty and mystery of the ships,
   And the magic of the sea.
      And the voice of that wayward song
      Is singing and saying still:
   "A boy's will is the wind's will,
And the thoughts of youth are long, long
     thoughts."

I remember the bulwarks by the shore,
 And the fort upon the hill;
The sun-rise gun, with its hollow roar,
The drum-beat, repeated o'er and o'er,
 And the bugle wild and shrill.
  And the music of that old song
  Throbs in my memory still:
 "A boy's will is the wind's will,
And the thoughts of youth are long, long
   thoughts."

I remember the sea-fight far away,
 How it thundered o'er the tide!
And the dead captains, as they lay
In their graves, o'erlooking the tranquil bay,
 Where they in battle died.
  And the sound of that mournful song
  Goes through me with a thrill:
 "A boy's will is the wind's will,
And the thoughts of youth are long, long
   thoughts."

I can see the breezy dome of groves,
   The shadows of Deering's Woods;
And the friendships old and the early loves
Come back with a sabbath sound, as of doves
   In quiet neighborhoods.
      And the verse of that sweet old song,
      It flutters and murmurs still:
   "A boy's will is the wind's will,
And the thoughts of youth are long, long
      thoughts."

I remember the gleams and glooms that dart
   Across the schoolboy's brain;
The song and the silence in the heart,
That in part are prophecies, and in part
   Are longings wild and vain.
      And the voice of that fitful song
      Sings on, and is never still:
   "A boy's will is the wind's will,
And the thoughts of youth are long, long
      thoughts."

There are things of which I may not speak;
  There are dreams that cannot die;
There are thoughts that make the strong heart
      weak,
And bring a pallor into the cheek,
  And a mist before the eye.
      And the words of that fatal song
      Come over me like a chill:
  "A boy's will is the wind's will,
And the thoughts of youth are long, long
      thoughts."

Strange to me now are the forms I meet
  When I visit the dear old town;
But the native air is pure and sweet,
And the trees that o'ershadow each well-known
      street,
  As they balance up and down,
      Are singing the beautiful song,
      Are sighing and whispering still:

"A boy's will is the wind's will,
And the thoughts of youth are long, long
      thoughts."

And Deering's Woods are fresh and fair,
    And with joy that is almost pain
My heart goes back to wander there,
And among the dreams of the days that were,
    I find my lost youth again.
      And the strange and beautiful song,
      The groves are repeating it still:
"A boy's will is the wind's will,
And the thoughts of youth are long, long
      thoughts."

THE ROPEWALK.

In that building, long and low,
With its windows all a-row,
   Like the port-holes of a hulk,
Human spiders spin and spin,
Backward down their threads so thin
   Dropping, each a hempen bulk.

At the end, an open door;
Squares of sunshine on the floor
   Light the long and dusky lane;
And the whirring of a wheel,
Dull and drowsy, makes me feel
   All its spokes are in my brain.

As the spinners to the end
Downward go and reascend,
   Gleam the long threads in the sun;
While within this brain of mine
Cobwebs brighter and more fine
   By the busy wheel are spun.

Two fair maidens in a swing,
Like white doves upon the wing,
   First before my vision pass;
Laughing, as their gentle hands
Closely clasp the twisted strands,
   At their shadow on the grass.

Then a booth of mountebanks,
With its smell of tan and planks,
   And a girl poised high in air
On a cord, in spangled dress,
With a faded loveliness,
   And a weary look of care.

Then a homestead among farms,
And a woman with bare arms
 Drawing water from a well;
As the bucket mounts apace,
With it mounts her own fair face,
 As at some magician's spell.

Then an old man in a tower,
Ringing loud the noontide hour,
 While the rope coils round and round
Like a serpent at his feet,
And again, in swift retreat,
 Nearly lifts him from the ground.

Then within a prison-yard,
Faces fixed, and stern, and hard,
 Laughter and indecent mirth;
Ah! it is the gallows-tree!
Breath of Christian charity,
 Blow, and sweep it from the earth!

Then a school-boy, with his kite
Gleaming in a sky of light,
    And an eager, upward look;
Steeds pursued through lane and field;
Fowlers with their snares concealed;
    And an angler by a brook.

Ships rejoicing in the breeze,
Wrecks that float o'er unknown seas,
    Anchors dragged through faithless sand;
Sea-fog drifting overhead,
And, with lessening line and lead,
    Sailors feeling for the land.

All these scenes do I behold,
These, and many left untold,
    In that building long and low;
While the wheel goes round and round,
With a drowsy, dreamy sound,
    And the spinners backward go.

THE GOLDEN MILE-STONE.

———

LEAFLESS are the trees; their purple branches
Spread themselves abroad, like reefs of coral,
     Rising silent
In the Red Sea of the Winter sunset.

From the hundred chimneys of the village,
Like the Afreet in the Arabian story,
     Smoky columns
Tower aloft into the air of amber.

At the window winks the flickering fire-light;
Here and there the lamps of evening glimmer,
      Social watch-fires
Answering one another through the darkness.

On the hearth the lighted logs are glowing,
And like Ariel in the cloven pine-tree
      For its freedom
Groans and sighs the air imprisoned in them.

By the fireside there are old men seated,
Seeing ruined cities in the ashes,
      Asking sadly
Of the Past what it can ne'er restore them.

By the fireside there are youthful dreamers,
Building castles fair, with stately stairways,
      Asking blindly
Of the Future what it cannot give them.

By the fireside tragedies are acted
In whose scenes appear two actors only,
      Wife and husband,
And above them God the sole spectator.

By the fireside there are peace and comfort,
Wives and children, with fair, thoughtful faces,
      Waiting, watching
For a well-known footstep in the passage.

Each man's chimney is his Golden Mile-stone;
Is the central point, from which he measures
      Every distance
Through the gateways of the world around him.

In his farthest wanderings still he sees it;
Hears the talking flame, the answering night-
      wind,
      As he heard them
When he sat with those who were, but are not.

Happy he whom neither wealth nor fashion,
Nor the march of the encroaching city,
     Drives an exile
From the hearth of his ancestral homestead.

We may build more splendid habitations,
Fill our rooms with paintings and with sculptures,
     But we cannot
Buy with gold the old associations!

CATAWBA WINE.

———

THIS song of mine
Is a Song of the Vine,
To be sung by the glowing embers
Of wayside inns,
When the rain begins
To darken the drear Novembers.

It is not a song
Of the Scuppernong,
From warm Carolinian valleys,
Nor the Isabel
And the Muscadel
That bask in our garden alleys.

Nor the red Mustang,
Whose clusters hang
O'er the waves of the Colorado,
And the fiery flood
Of whose purple blood
Has a dash of Spanish bravado.

For richest and best
Is the wine of the West,
That grows by the Beautiful River;
Whose sweet perfume
Fills all the room
With a benison on the giver.

And as hollow trees
Are the haunts of bees,
Forever going and coming;
So this crystal hive
Is all alive
With a swarming and buzzing and humming.

Very good in its way
Is the Verzenay,
Or the Sillery soft and creamy;
But Catawba wine
Has a taste more divine,
More dulcet, delicious, and dreamy.

There grows no vine
By the haunted Rhine,
By Danube or Guadalquivir,
Nor on island or cape,
That bears such a grape
As grows by the Beautiful River.

Drugged is their juice
For foreign use,
When shipped o'er the reeling Atlantic,
To rack our brains
With the fever pains,
That have driven the Old World frantic.

To the sewers and sinks
With all such drinks,
And after them tumble the mixer;
For a poison malign
Is such Borgia wine,
Or at best but a Devil's Elixir.

While pure as a spring
Is the wine I sing,
And to praise it, one needs but name it;
For Catawba wine
Has need of no sign,
No tavern-bush to proclaim it.

And this Song of the Vine,
This greeting of mine,
The winds and the birds shall deliver
To the Queen of the West,
In her garlands dressed,
On the banks of the Beautiful River.

SANTA FILOMENA.

———

WHENE'ER a noble deed is wrought,
Whene'er is spoken a noble thought,
　　Our hearts, in glad surprise,
　　To higher levels rise.

The tidal wave of deeper souls
Into our inmost being rolls,
　　And lifts us unawares
　　Out of all meaner cares.

Honor to those whose words or deeds
Thus help us in our daily needs,
　　And by their overflow
　　Raise us from what is low!

Thus thought I, as by night I read
Of the great army of the dead,
    The trenches cold and damp,
    The starved and frozen camp,—

The wounded from the battle-plain,
In dreary hospitals of pain,
    The cheerless corridors,
    The cold and stony floors.

Lo! in that house of misery
A lady with a lamp I see
    Pass through the glimmering gloom,
    And flit from room to room.

And slow, as in a dream of bliss,
The speechless sufferer turns to kiss
    Her shadow, as it falls
    Upon the darkening walls.

As if a door in heaven should be
Opened and then closed suddenly,
    The vision came and went,
    The light shone and was spent.

On England's annals, through the long
Hereafter of her speech and song,
    That light its rays shall cast
    From portals of the past.

A Lady with a Lamp shall stand
In the great history of the land,
    A noble type of good,
    Heroic womanhood.

Nor even shall be wanting here
The palm, the lily, and the spear,
    The symbols that of yore
    Saint Filomena bore.

DAYBREAK.

A WIND came up out of the sea,
And said, "O mists, make room for me."

It hailed the ships, and cried, "Sail on,
Ye mariners, the night is gone."

And hurried landward far away,
Crying, "Awake! it is the day."

It said unto the forest, "Shout!
Hang all your leafy banners out!"

It touched the wood-bird's folded wing,
And said, "O bird, awake and sing."

And o'er the farms, "O chanticleer,
Your clarion blow; the day is near."

It whispered to the fields of corn,
"Bow down, and hail the coming morn."

It shouted through the belfry-tower,
"Awake, O bell! proclaim the hour."

It crossed the churchyard with a sigh,
And said, "Not yet! in quiet lie."